My Picture Dictionary

by Hale C. Reid
Helen W. Crane

Ginn and Company

Aa Bb Cc Dd

Ee Ff Gg Hh

Ii Jj Kk Ll

Mm Nn Oo Pp

Qq Rr Ss Tt

Uu Vv Ww Xx

Yy Zz

2

Home Office, Lexington, Massachusetts 02
0-663-42378-3

A a

airport

apple

a

about

across

after

again

all

always

am

an

and

another

any

are

around

as

asked

at

ate

away

B b

baby

baseball

bag

basket

ball

bear

balloon

bed

barn

bee

B b

bell

bicycle

bird

birthday

boat

book

box

boys

bread

brook

B b

bug

bunny

bus

button

back

be

because

best

better

big

bite

bring

build

bump

but

buy

buzzed

by

C c

cake

chair

candle

chicks

candy

children

car

circus

cat

clock

7

C c

clown

coat

cookies

corn

cowboy

call

came

can

can't

catch

city

cold

color

come

coming

could

crying

Dd

dog

doll

dress

duck

day
did
didn't
dinner
do
don't
down
drop
during

Ee

eggs

eat
every

F f

farm

flowers

father

feather

fire

fish

face
fast
faster
find
for
found
friend
from
fun
funny

girls

goat

grandfather

grandmother

groceries

game

gave

get

getting

give

go

going

gone

good

good-by

got

guess

H h

hamburger

hand

hat

heart

helicopter

hen

hill

home

honey

horn

H h

horse

house

hear

heard

help

her

here

hide

high

him

his

hot

how

hurry

had

happen

happy

has

have

he

ice

ice cream

iron

I
if
I'm
in
is
it
it's

jeep

jet

jingle
job
jump
just

key

kitten

king

knife

kitchen

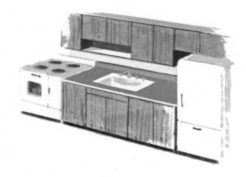

keep

kept

kind

knew

knock

know

kite

lamb

leaves

letter

lion

lunch

laughed

learn

let

let's

like

little

live

long

look

lost

lot

love

Mm

mailbox

man

meat

milk

mitten

money

moon

mother

mountain

Mm

mouse

machine
made
make
many
may
maybe
me
men
met

middle
might
mill
miss
more
morning
most
Mr.
Mrs.
much
must
my

nail

nest

newspaper

nickel

nuts

name
need
never
new
next
nice
night
no
noise
not
nothing
now

Oo

ocean

orange

owl

o'clock
of
off
often

oh
old
on
once
only
open
or
other
our
out
over
own

20

Pp

pan

pennies

pancakes

people

paper

pets

park

picnic

pencil

pig

Pp

pocket

puppy

pole

policeman

pony

postman

paint

party

plant

play

please

pop

pretty

puddle

put

Qq

quarter

queen

quack

question

quick

quiet

Rr

rabbit

rain

rooster

race

ran

ready

ride

ring

rolled

run

S s

saddle

seesaw

Santa Claus

sheep

satellite

shoe

school

skate

sky

scissors

S s

sled

squirrel

snake

star

snow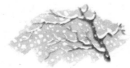

store

snowman

street

sprinkler

streetcar

S s

sun

said
sang
sat
saw
say
see
she
show
side
sing

sleep
so
some
something
soon
splash
started
stay
step
stop
story
surprise

table

television

taxi

top

teacher

town

teeth

toys

telephone

tractor

T t

train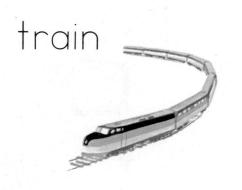

tree

truck

turkey

turtle

take

than

thank

that

the

their

them

then

there

they

thing

think

28

T t

this	today
three	tomorrow
time	too
tiny	took
to	two

U u

umbrella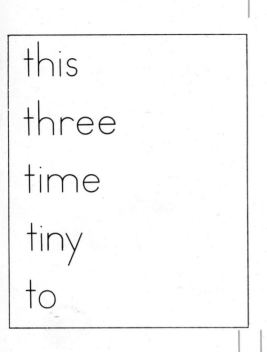

up
us

V v

valentine

very
visiting
voice

W w

wagon

window

watch

wolf

wheat

woman

wheel

woods

whistle

world

W w

wait	what
walk	when
want	where
warm	who
was	will
wash	win
water	wish
way	with
we	wonderful
well	word
went	work
were	would

xylophone

x as in:

box

fox

yard

yes

you

your

zoo

zero

zoom

Action Words

climb   hop   run

swim   swing

skip   dance   walk

jump   skate

Parts of the Body

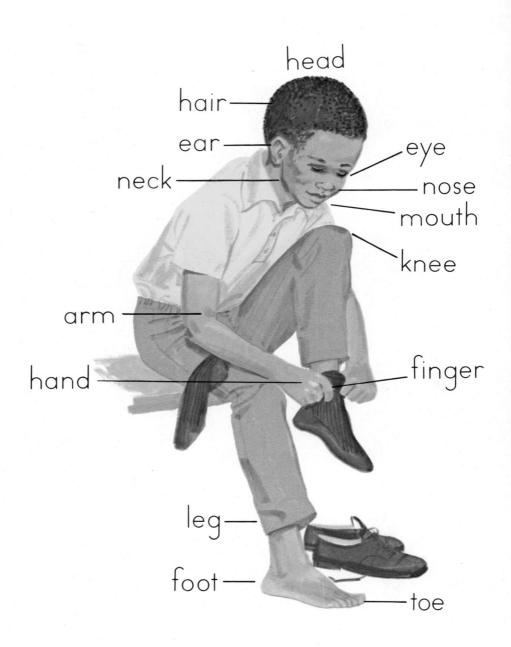

head

hair

ear

neck

eye

nose

mouth

knee

arm

hand

finger

leg

foot

toe

The Family

mother father

sister

baby

brother

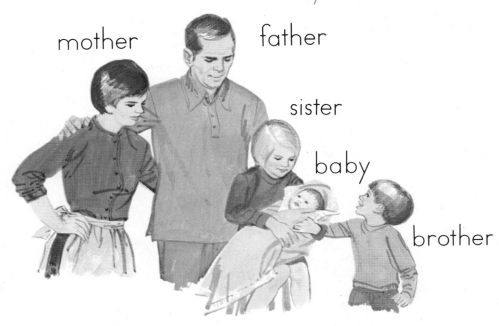

cousins aunt uncle

grandmother

grandfather

Toys

doll   kite   drum

train   ball

car   truck   boat

wagon   bicycle

Helpful Little Words

Farm

haystack

tractor

silo

barn

farmhouse

pump

pigs

fence

garden

cow

calf

grass

chickens

pony

buildings

apartments

traffic light

hotel

department store

bank

post office

policeman

car

bus

mailbox

fire hydrant

street

sidewalk

Fruits

plum   orange   lemon

banana   grapes

cherry   pear   apple

strawberry   peach

Vegetables

potato   peas   onion

celery   squash

beans   beet   cabbage

lettuce   carrot

Weather

moon   stars   sun

snow   sky

wind   clouds   rain

lightning   rainbow

Kinds of Workers

farmer

fire fighter

dentist

police officer

ous driver

teacher

doctor

mail carrier

Animals

rabbit

bear

monkey

fox

raccoon

elephant

seal

tiger

lion

beaver

Number Zoo

1 one

2 two

3 three

4 four

5 five

6 six

7 seven

8 eight

9 nine

10 ten

Days of the Week

Sunday
Monday
Tuesday
Wednesday
Thursday
Friday
Saturday

Colors

yellow green blue orange

red brown white black

Months and Holidays

January	February	March
New Year's Day 	Valentine's Day 	

April	May	June
	Mother's Day 	Father's Day 

July	August	September
Fourth of July 		

October	November	December
Halloween 	Thanksgiving Day 	Christmas Day 

47

NOTE TO PARENTS AND TEACHERS

My Picture Dictionary is designed to help small children help themselves in writing and spelling. It also introduces the dictionary habit, which can and should be encouraged as early as the first grade. As children use the illustrations to locate words in this simple dictionary, they learn that words have printed symbols and can be arranged alphabetically. Usually this experience is their first contact with words in an alphabetical arrangement.

Selection of Content

The 175 nouns illustrated in this dictionary were selected from 2800 different words found in 4500 independently written compositions of 1500 first-grade children. The additional 274 words in the body of the dictionary are among those that appeared with high frequency in these compositions. The entire word list has been closely correlated with the vocabulary of the early books in the Ginn reading programs.

Included in this dictionary are also sixteen classification pages of pictured words such as "Toys," "Fruits," and "Animals." These pages add 133 more words to the dictionary.

Format

The pictured words are listed first under each guide letter. The words that do not lend themselves to illustration are alphabetized separately in easily distinguishable columns.

The entries are in manuscript writing such as the children will be learning and using. The single-word entry makes it easy for first- or second-grade children to find the words they need in their early composition work. Guide letters, both capital and small, help the pupils locate the words they want to write.

The illustrations appear below or beside the entry words. Their simplicity helps pupils acquire precise meanings.

Suggestions for Helping Children

When children ask for the spelling of a word, help them to identify the initial letter, as *b* in *boat*. Then help them to find the pages on which the words beginning with that letter are pictured.

Using the dictionary to find out how words are spelled will help the children recognize that words beginning with the same sound often start with the same letter.

Although it is not necessary for children to know the alphabet to look up a word, they will soon learn it through constant use.

The use of *My Picture Dictionary* enables pupils to progress at their own speed in writing activities and thus helps the teacher to provide for individual needs and abilities.

CDEFGHIJ0898765

PRINTED IN THE UNITED STATES OF AMERICA